Know Your Maths

CONTENTS

Miles Kelly

TIMES TABLES

Multiplication is commutative. That means the order that we multiply numbers doesn't matter – the product (answer) will always be the same.

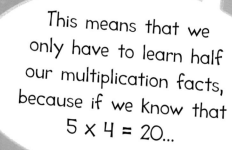

We can make four calculations from one multiplication. Trace the example below.

This means that we only have to learn half our multiplication facts, because if we know that 5 × 4 = 20...

$$6 \times 2 = 12$$
$$2 \times 6 = 12$$

...we also know that 4 × 5 = 20!

Division is the inverse (opposite) of multiplication. The answer to a division is called the quotient.

$$12 \div 2 = 6$$
$$12 \div 6 = 2$$

$$1 \times 1 = 1$$

This calculation shows 1 group of 1, or 1 multiplied 1 time.

I'm holding 1 shell.

There are two ways to find out how many shells I'm holding.

① Count the number of groups. There is 1. Count the number of shells. There are 2.

② Count the number of shells. There are 2. Count the number of groups. There is 1.

$$1 \times 2 = 2$$

$$2 \times 1 = 2$$

This means 1 group of 2 shells.

This means 2 shells multiplied 1 time.

Well done!

5

There are two ways to find out how many starfish the diver has.

There is 1 group.
There are 3 starfish.

$$1 \times 3 = 3$$

This means 1 group of 3 starfish.

There are 3 starfish.
There is 1 group.

$$3 \times 1 = 3$$

This means 3 starfish multiplied 1 time.

Draw more starfish to show $1 \times 3 = 3$ or $3 \times 1 = 3$

Draw more starfish to show $1 \times 4 = 4$ or $4 \times 1 = 4$

$$1 \times 4 = 4$$

$$4 \times 1 = 4$$

Complete the calculations – trace the numbers and
then write the correct numbers in the boxes.

Trace the right number
of starfish to go with the first
calculation, then wipe them
clean and do the same for
the others.

5 × 1 = ☐   9 × 1 = ☐

1 × 6 = ☐   1 × 10 = ☐

7 × 1 = ☐   11 × 1 = ☐

1 × 8 = ☐   1 × 12 = ☐

Well done!

7

The number of patches on this turtle's shell shows us two calculations.

$$1 \times 5 = 5$$

$$5 \times 1 = 5$$

What two calculations do these turtles' shells show? Trace the numbers and write the correct numbers in the boxes.

$$\boxed{} \times \boxed{} = 6$$

$$\boxed{} \times \boxed{} = 6$$

$$\boxed{} \times \boxed{} = 8$$

$$\boxed{} \times \boxed{} = 8$$

Fill in the missing numbers.

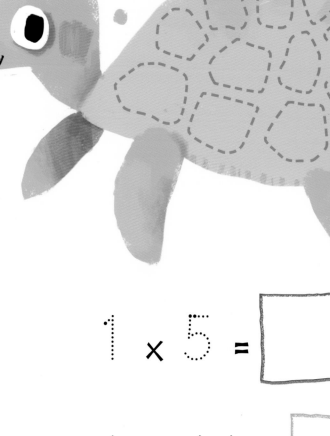

Use my shell to trace the right number of patches to go with each calculation.

1 × ⬜ = 9

1 × 5 = ⬜

2 × ⬜ = 2

1 × 11 = ⬜

1 × ⬜ = 8

⬜ × 1 = 1

1 × ⬜ = 10

⬜ × 1 = 7

12 × ⬜ = 12

⬜ × 3 = 3

Well done!

Division is the inverse (opposite) of multiplication. When we divide we make equal groups.

$$1 \div 1 = 1$$

$$2 \div 1 = 2$$

I can make 1 group of 1 shell.

I can make 1 group of 2 shells.

Unlike multiplication, division is not commutative – the answer is different depending on the order in which we divide the numbers.

$$2 \div 1 = 2$$

$$1 \div 2 = \frac{1}{2}$$

I can make 1 group of 2 shells.

I only have one shell but I need a group of 2 – I don't have enough!

Complete the calculations – trace the numbers and write the correct numbers in the boxes.

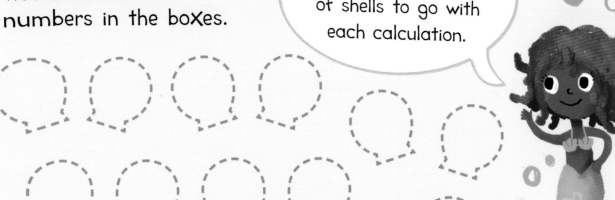

Use this space to trace the right number of shells to go with each calculation.

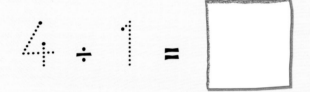

$4 \div 1 = $ ☐

$5 \div 1 = $ ☐

$6 \div 1 = $ ☐

$7 \div 1 = $ ☐

$8 \div 1 = $ ☐

$9 \div 1 = $ ☐

$10 \div 1 = $ ☐

$11 \div 1 = $ ☐

$12 \div 1 = $ ☐

Well done! ✓

11

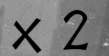

×2

$1 \times 2 = 2$

$2 \times 1 = 2$

We've seen these calculations before – on page 5!

$2 \times 2 = 4$

This calculation shows that together we have 2 groups of 2 spots, or 2 multiplied by 2.

I have 1 group of 2 spots.

There are two ways to find out how many spots the two rays below have altogether.

You can count the number of groups, and then count the number of spots on each group.

Or you can count the number of spots in each group first, and then count the number of groups.

There are 2 groups of 3 spots.

There are 3 spots and 2 groups.

$2 \times 3 = 6$

$3 \times 2 = 6$

Use both ways to find out how many spots these groups of rays have.

Groups:

Spots in each group:

Spots in each group:

Groups:

$2 \times 4 = 8$

$4 \times 2 = 8$

Complete the calculations by writing the correct numbers in the boxes.

Fill in the right number of spots to go with each calculation.

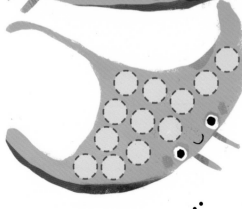

$5 \times 2 = $ ☐

$12 \times 2 = $ ☐

$2 \times 8 = $ ☐

$7 \times 2 = $ ☐

$2 \times 6 = $ ☐

$9 \times 2 = $ ☐

$11 \times 2 = $ ☐

$2 \times 10 = $ ☐

Well done!

13

Use both ways to find out how many stripes
these two lobsters have altogether.

Groups: ☐

Stripes in each group: ☐

Stripes in each group: ☐

Groups: ☐

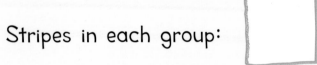 2 × 5 = ☐   5 × 2 = ☐

What two calculations do the stripes on these lobsters show?

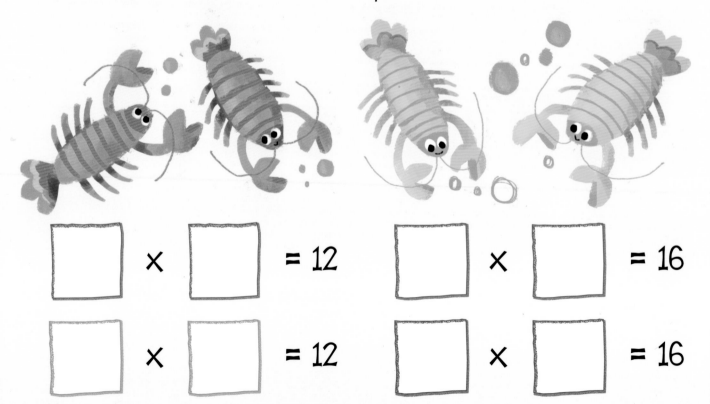

☐ × ☐ = 12   ☐ × ☐ = 16

☐ × ☐ = 12   ☐ × ☐ = 16

14

Complete the calculations by writing the correct numbers in the boxes.

Use our backs to trace the right number of stripes to go with each calculation.

☐ × 2 = 8

☐ × 2 = 14

☐ × 2 = 6

☐ × 2 = 2

12 × ☐ = 24

2 × ☐ = 4

2 × ☐ = 20

2 × ☐ = 18

2 × 11 = ☐

Well done! ⋰

15

÷ 2

How many groups of spines do these pufferfish have?

I can make 1 group of 2 spines.

$$2 \div 2 = 1$$

$$4 \div 2 = 2$$

We can make 2 groups of 2 spines.

We can make 3 groups of 2 spines.

$$6 \div 2 = 3$$

Complete the calculations by writing the correct numbers in the boxes.

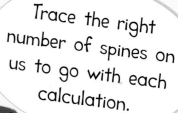

Trace the right number of spines on us to go with each calculation.

8 ÷ 2 = ☐

18 ÷ 2 = ☐

24 ÷ 2 = ☐

10 ÷ 2 = ☐

20 ÷ 2 = ☐

16 ÷ 2 = ☐

12 ÷ 2 = ☐

22 ÷ 2 = ☐

A group of pufferfish have 14 spines altogether. If each pufferfish has two spines, how many pufferfish are in the group?

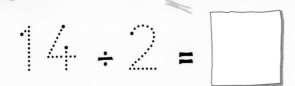

Trace us to help you!

14 ÷ 2 = ☐

Well done! ✓

× 5

$1 × 5 = 5$

We've seen all these calculations before!

$2 × 5 = 10$

$5 × 1 = 5$

$5 × 2 = 10$

I have 1 group of 5 bubbles.

We have 2 groups of 5 bubbles.

There are two ways to find out how many bubbles the group of fish below have.

You can count the number of groups first, and then count the number of bubbles in each group.

Or you can count the number of bubbles in each group first, and then count the number of groups.

There are 3 groups of 5 bubbles.

There are 5 bubbles and 3 groups.

$3 × 5 = 15$

$5 × 3 = 15$

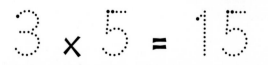

Use both ways to find out how many bubbles these fish have.

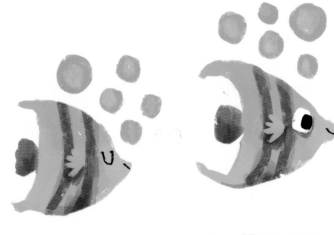

Groups: [ ]

Bubbles in each group: [ ]

Bubbles in each group: [ ]

Groups: [ ]

$4 \times 5 = 20$

$5 \times 4 = 20$

Use both ways to find out how many bubbles these fish have.

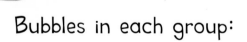

Groups: [ ]

Bubbles in each group: [ ]

Bubbles in each group: [ ]

Groups: [ ]

$5 \times 5 = 25$

$5 \times 5 = 25$

Well done!

Write numbers in the boxes and draw more pearls in these shells to help you complete the calculations below.

Groups:

Pearls in each group:

Pearls in each group:

Groups:

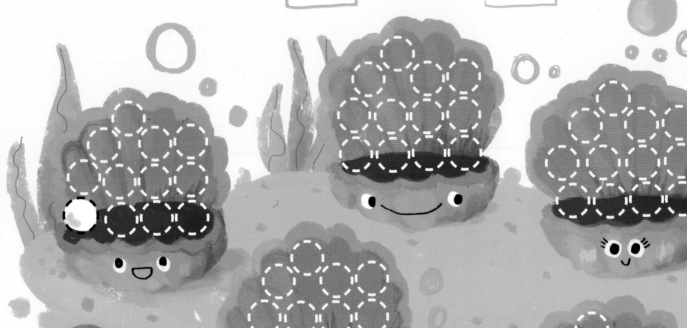

5 × 6 =

9 × 5 =

7 × 5 =

5 × 10 =

5 × 8 =

11 × 5 =

5 × 12 =

20

Fill in the missing numbers.

Draw pearls in us to help you!

$\boxed{} \times 5 = 35$

$\boxed{} \times 8 = 40$

$3 \times 5 = \boxed{}$

$11 \times 5 = \boxed{}$

$10 \times 5 = \boxed{}$

$12 \times \boxed{} = 60$

$5 \times \boxed{} = 55$

$5 \times \boxed{} = 40$

$5 \times \boxed{} = 25$

$4 \times \boxed{} = 20$

$5 \times \boxed{} = 30$

$5 \times \boxed{} = 25$

Well done!

How many groups of scales do these fish have?

$$5 \div 5 = 1$$

I can make 1 group of 5 scales.

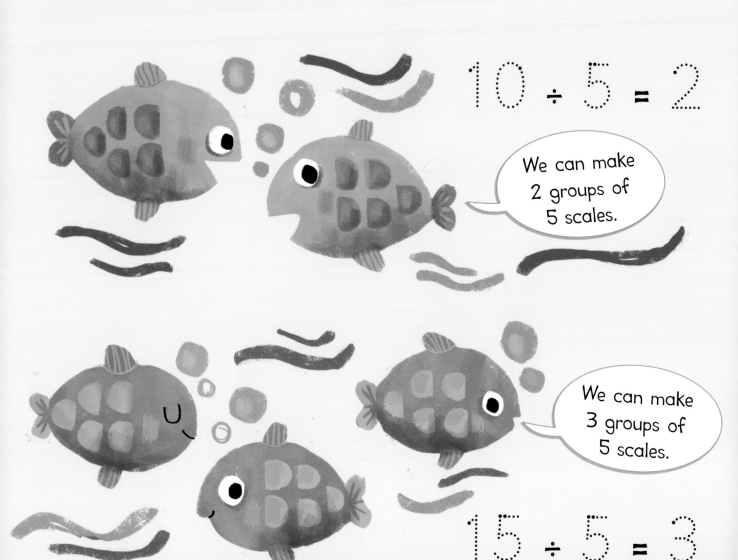

$$10 \div 5 = 2$$

We can make 2 groups of 5 scales.

We can make 3 groups of 5 scales.

$$15 \div 5 = 3$$

Complete the calculations by writing the correct numbers in the boxes.

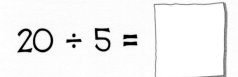

Draw 5 scales on the right number of us to go with each calculation.

20 ÷ 5 = ☐   25 ÷ 5 = ☐   30 ÷ 5 = ☐

35 ÷ 5 = ☐   40 ÷ 5 = ☐   45 ÷ 5 = ☐

50 ÷ 5 = ☐   55 ÷ 5 = ☐   60 ÷ 5 = ☐

A group of fish have 35 scales altogether. If each fish has five scales, how many fish are in the group?

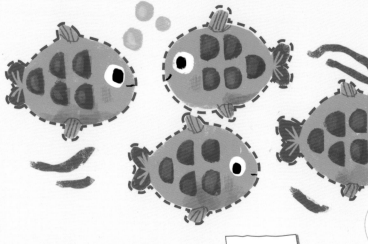

Trace us to help you!

35 ÷ 5 = ☐

Well done! ✓

23

× 10 and ÷ 10

I need to multiply 10 octopuses by 1.

Try drawing circles instead. 1 circle represents 1 octopus. This is called an array.

It will take me a long time to draw 10!

This array shows these two calculations:

$$10 \times 1 = 10$$
$$1 \times 10 = 10$$

It also helps us to see:

$$10 \div 10 = 1$$
$$10 \div 1 = 10$$

This is another array:

It shows these two calculations:

$$10 \times 2 = 20$$
$$2 \times 10 = 20$$

It also helps us to see:

$$20 \div 10 = 2$$
$$20 \div 2 = 10$$

What four facts does this array show?

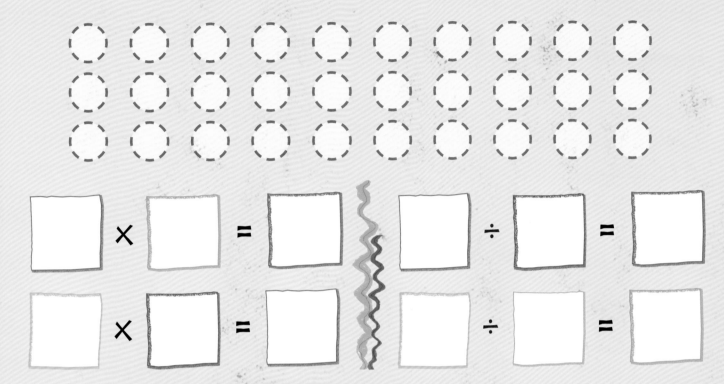

What four facts does this array show?

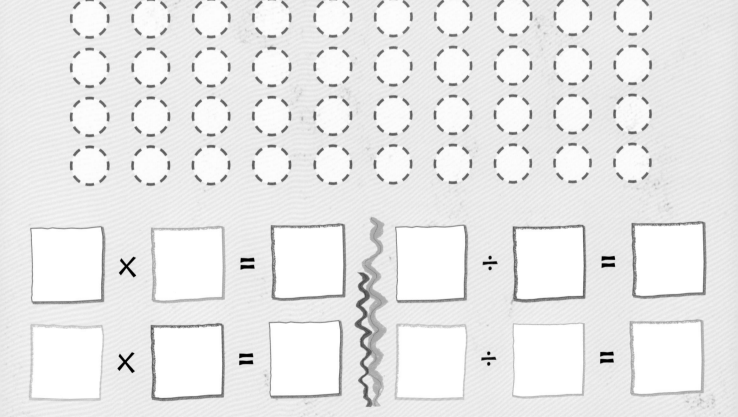

Well done! ✓

PROBLEM SOLVING

A bar model is a way to show a maths problem that requires the use of an addition, subtraction, multiplication or division calculation to solve it. It doesn't give you the answer to the calculation, but it helps you understand which type of calculation you need to use. In bar models we use squares to represent individual units.

This square represents the number of spots I have.

I have twice as many spots, so we draw two squares to show this.

This bar model helps us to work out how many spots the butterflies have altogether. It helps us see that they have 4 + 4 + 4, or 4 × 3.

Trace the numbers in the bar models, then use the completed models to solve the problems. Look at the pictures for help if you get stuck.

Bats has 3 flowers. Spike has twice as many. We can draw a bar model to show how many flowers Bats and Spike have *altogether*.

The bar model helps us see that we have 3 + 3 + 3. This can also be written as 3 × 3.

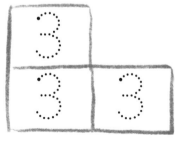

Bats

Spike

How many flowers do they have altogether?

What if Bats has 5 flowers and Spike has twice as many?

Bats  5

Spike 5 5

How many flowers do they have altogether?

What if Bats has 6 flowers and I have twice as many?

Bats 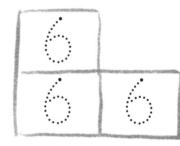 6

Spike 6 6

How many flowers do they have altogether?

Well done!

27

Trace the numbers, then write the correct numbers in the bottom row of the bar models. Use the completed models to solve the problems.

Squid has 5 arms. Jelly has 3 times as many. Fill in the bar model to show this.

Squid

Jelly

How many arms do they have altogether?

Glub has 2 stripes. Trumpet has 3 times as many. Fill in the bar model to show this.

Glub

Trumpet

How many stripes do they have altogether?

28

Scrute has 4 eyes.
Scope has 3 times
as many. Fill in
the bar model
to show this.

Scrute | 4 |
Scope | | | |

How many eyes do they have altogether?

Jot has 3 spots.
Smudge has
3 times as many.
Fill in the bar
model to show this.

Jot | 3 |
Smudge | | | |

How many spots do
they have altogether?

Well done!

29

Trace the numbers, then write the correct numbers in the bottom row of the bar models. Use the completed models to solve the problems.

The bar model helps us see that we have 5 + 10.

Yum has 5 sweets. Scrump has 10 sweets. We can draw a bar model to show this.

Yum	Scrump
5	10
15	

How many sweets do they have altogether?

What if Yum has 6 sweets?

Yum	Scrump
6	10

You could draw one more sweet to help you.

How many sweets do they have altogether?

30

Fill in the blank bar model to help you solve the first problem on this page. Then wipe it clean and use it to help you solve the next problem.

Yum   Scrump

10

What if I have 7 sweets?

How many sweets do they have altogether?

Yum has ⬜ sweets.

Make up your own number of sweets that I might have, and solve the problem.

How many sweets do they have altogether?

Well done!

31

Splodge has 6 cans of paint. Splatter has 7 cans of paint.

We can draw a bar model to show how many they have altogether.

Splodge   Splatter

How many cans of paint do they have altogether?

Doodle has 6 pencils. Scribble has 8 pencils.

Doodle   Scribble

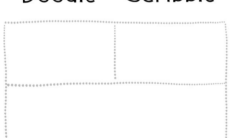

We can see that we need to add 6 and 8.

How many pencils do they have altogether?

32

Draw your own bar models and fill them in to show and solve the problems.

Smash has 6 blocks.
Topple has 9 blocks.

Draw your bar model here

How many blocks do they have altogether?

Quiz has 6 books. Cram has 10 books.

Draw your bar model here

ow many books do
hey have altogether?

Well done!

33

Lix ate 11 cakes. Bolt ate 6 cakes. We can draw a bar model to show how many *more* cakes Lix ate.

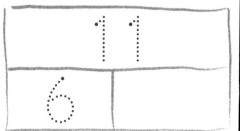

We need to find the difference between 11 and 6. Cross out 6 of these cakes to help you.

Lix ate [ ] more cakes.

If you need help, draw 1 more cake in the group above, then cross out 6 to find the difference.

What if most of the problem stays the same but Lix ate 12 cakes?

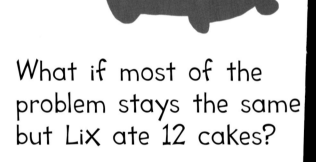

Lix ate [ ] more cakes.

34

Fill in the blank bar model to help you solve the first problem on this page. Then wipe it clean and use it to help you solve the next problem.

What if I eat 13 cakes?

Lix ate ☐ more cakes.

Make up your own number of cakes that Lix could have eaten. Solve the problem!

Lix ate ☐ cakes.

Lix ate ☐ more cakes.

Well done!

Trace the numbers and dotted lines, then fill in the bar models. Use the completed models to solve the problems.

Laze read 7 pages of her book. Splash read 5. We can draw a bar model to show how many *more* pages Laze read.

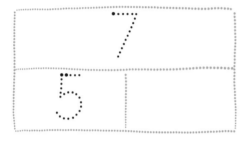

Laze read ☐ more pages.

Scoop built 8 sandcastles. Doug built 5 sandcastles.

Scoop built ☐ more sandcastles.

Fill in the blank bar model to help you solve the first problem on this page. Then wipe it clean and use it to help you solve the next problem.

Rocky ate 4 ice creams. Neo ate 2. How many more ice creams did Rocky eat?

What if I eat 5 ice creams?

Rocky ate ☐ more ice creams.

Make up your own number of ice creams that Rocky could have eaten. Solve the problem!

Rocky ate ☐ ice creams.

Rocky ate ☐ more ice creams.

Well done! .∵

37

Draw your own bar models to show and solve the problems.

Hertz practised music for 9 minutes. Mono practised music for 5 minutes.

Draw your bar model here

How many more minutes did Hertz practise for?

Buzz spent 12 minutes playing music.
Patch spent 7 minutes playing music.

Draw your bar model here

How many more minutes did Buzz play for?

Tempo spent 10 minutes playing guitar.
Reverb spent 6 minutes playing guitar.

Draw your bar model here

How many more minutes
did Tempo play for?

Buddy spent 15 minutes playing the drums.
Bird spent 2 minutes playing the saxophone.

Draw your bar model here

ow many more minutes
d Buddy play for?

Well done!

Trace the numbers, then write the correct numbers in the bottom row of the bar models. Use the completed models to solve the problems.

Swish scored 13 points. Dribble scored 5 *more* points than Swish. We can draw a bar model to show how many points Dribble scored.

13	5

To find out how many points Dribble scored we need to add 13 and 5.

Dribble scored ⬚ points.

What if the problem stays the same, but Dribble scored 6 more points than Swish?

13	6

Dribble scored ⬚ points.

Fill in the blank bar model to help you solve the first problem on this page. Then wipe it clean and use it to help you solve the next problem.

13

What if Dribble scored 7 more points than Swish?

Dribble scored ☐ points.

What if Dribble scored 8 more points than Swish?

Make up your own number of points more that Dribble could have scored. Solve the problem!

Dribble scored ☐ more points.

Dribble scored ☐ points.

Well done!

Trace the numbers and dotted lines, then write the correct numbers in the bottom row of the bar models. Use the completed models to solve the problems.

8	4

Zoom's car has 8 stripes.
Zip's has 4 more.

Zoom's car has [ ] stripes.

Add the right number of stripes to my car.

Beep's car has 7 hearts. Axle's car has 2 more.

7	2

Axle's car has [ ] hearts.

Add the right number of hearts to my car.

Bump's car has 12 stars. Prang's has 3 more.

12 | 3

Prang's car has ☐ stars.

Add the right number of stars to my car.

Spark's car has 9 spots. Trax's has 5 more.

9 | 5

Trax's car has ☐ spots.

Add the right number of spots to my car.

Well done! ✓

Draw your own bar models to show and solve these problems.

Grub has 8 carrots.
Fang has 6 more.

Draw your bar model here

Fang has carrots.

Goop has 8 pineapples.
Pep has 7 more.

Draw your bar model here

Pep has pineapples.

Bar models can show several calculations at once. The pink bar model to the right shows us four.

Subtraction is the inverse (opposite) of addition. Addition is the inverse of subtraction.

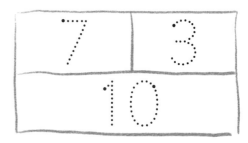

7	3
10	

Addition is commutative – no matter which order we add two numbers, the sum is always the same.

$7 + 3 = 10$

$3 + 7 = 10$

$10 - 3 = 7$

$10 - 7 = 3$

We can count on from 12 to 18 or count back from 18 to 12 to find the missing number.

We can use bar models to solve missing number problems.

12	
18	

$12 + \boxed{} = 18$

Well done!

45

Fill in the bar models and find the missing numbers in these calculations.

$20 - \boxed{} = 9$

$\boxed{} + 9 = 17$

$\boxed{} + 8 = 14$

46

7 + 6 =

Look for clues to help you in the picture.

___ - 5 = 12

___ + 7 = 18

Well done!

FRACTIONS

A fraction is part of a whole.

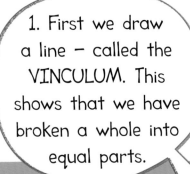

1. First we draw a line – called the VINCULUM. This shows that we have broken a whole into equal parts.

$$\frac{1}{2}$$

2. Next we write the bottom number – the DENOMINATOR. It shows how many equal parts there are. The fraction above has 2 equal parts. If 1 whole is divided into 2 equal parts we call each part a half.

3. Then we write the top number, the NUMERATOR. It shows how many equal parts we are thinking about. We are thinking about 1 of the 2 parts – 1 half.

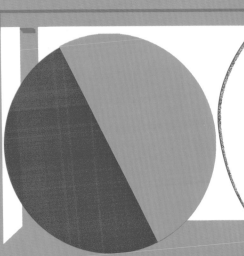

Here is a group of blocks.

$\frac{1}{2}$ of the blocks are red and $\frac{1}{2}$ of the blocks are yellow. If we put the blocks together we have one whole group. That's what this calculation shows:

Trace any dotted numbers and lines you see.

$$\frac{1}{2} + \frac{1}{2} = 1$$

Here is another group of blocks.

Draw 1 loop around the blue block and 1 loop around the green block.

 of the blocks are blue

 of the blocks are green

 + $\frac{1}{2}$ = 1

Draw 1 loop around the purple blocks and 1 loop around the orange blocks.

 of the blocks are purple

 of the blocks are orange

 + $\frac{1}{2}$ = 1

Draw 1 loop around the black blocks and 1 loop around the pink blocks.

 of the blocks are black

 of the blocks are pink

 + $\frac{1}{2}$ = 1

Well done!

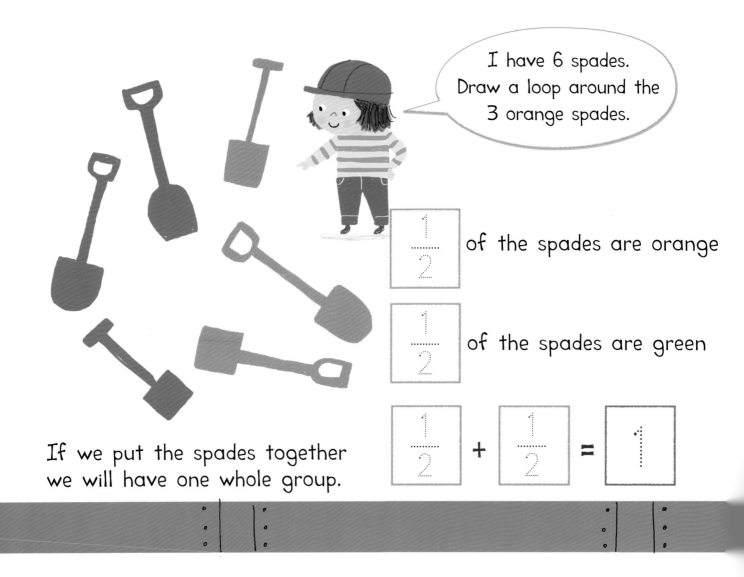

I have 6 spades. Draw a loop around the 3 orange spades.

$\frac{1}{2}$ of the spades are orange

$\frac{1}{2}$ of the spades are green

If we put the spades together we will have one whole group.

$\frac{1}{2} + \frac{1}{2} = 1$

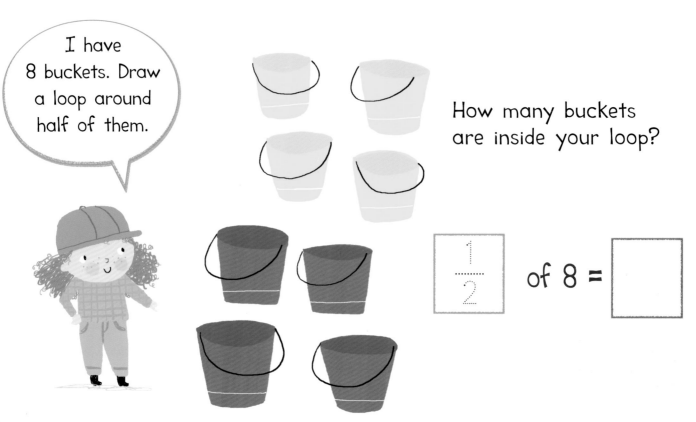

I have 8 buckets. Draw a loop around half of them.

How many buckets are inside your loop?

$\frac{1}{2}$ of 8 =

I have 10 windows. Draw a loop around half of them.

How many windows are inside your loop?

$\frac{1}{2}$ of 10 = ☐

I have 12 pipes. Draw a loop around half of them.

How many pipes are inside your loop?

$\frac{1}{2}$ of 12 = ☐

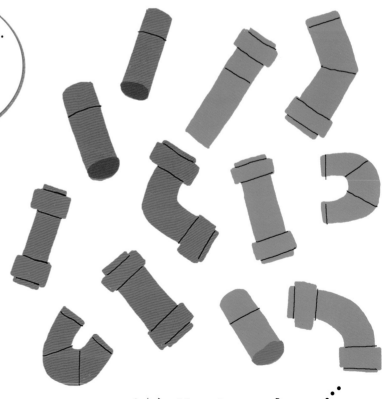

Well done!

51

Tick the flower beds on this page that show two halves.

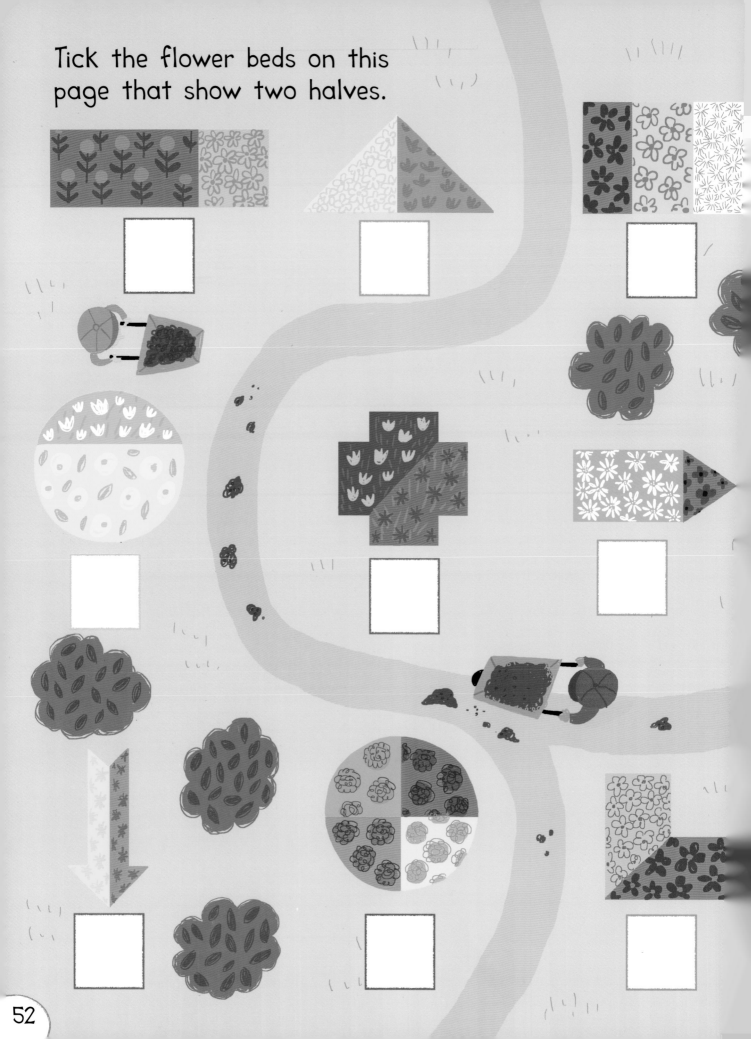

Draw a line to show half on each of the flower beds on this page.

Well done!

Write the correct numbers in the bar models to help you answer the questions on these two pages.

I'm planting trees. So far I've planted half of them. How many will there be when I'm finished?

6
3 | 3

How many trees will there will be altogether?

What if I've planted half of them now?

8
4 | 4

How many trees will there will be altogether?

I used half of some blocks to build a chimney. I used 4 blocks. How many blocks did I start with?

4

Use the bar model to show your answer.

There were ☐ blocks to start with.

I used half of some blocks to build a wall. I used 8 blocks. How many blocks did I start with?

8

Use the bar model to show your answer.

There were ☐ blocks to start with.

Draw lines from the crane that are half of the lengths below.

Using a ruler, draw the first line. Then write the correct number in the first box below.

Start your lines here

$\frac{1}{2}$ of 10 centimetres =

$\frac{1}{2}$ of 12 centimetres =

$\frac{1}{2}$ of 16 centimetres =

$\frac{1}{2}$ of 18 centimetres =

$\frac{1}{2}$ of 20 centimetres =

Wipe your first line away, then draw the next line, and fill in the next box, and so on.

Well done!

Look at this fraction. Do you think it is bigger or smaller than $\frac{1}{2}$?

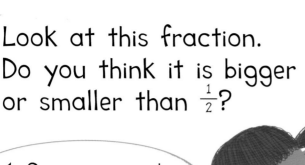

TOY FACTORY

1. Can you remember what this line is called? Look back to page 2 if you need help.

$$\frac{1}{4}$$

3. The NUMERATOR tells us we are thinking about 1 of the 4 equal parts – 1 quarter.

2. The DENOMINATOR tells us there are 4 equal parts. If 1 whole is divided into 4 equal parts we call each part a quarter, or 1 fourth.

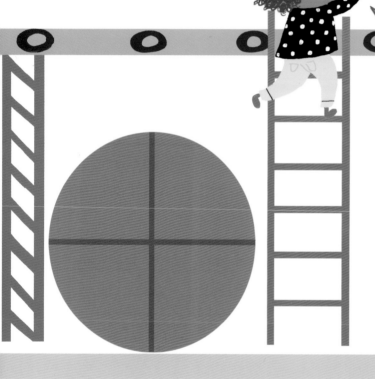

Here is a group of toy blocks.

$\frac{1}{4}$ of the blocks are yellow.
$\frac{3}{4}$ of the blocks are red.
If we put the blocks together we will have the whole group. That's what this calculation shows:

$$\frac{1}{4} + \frac{3}{4} = 1$$

Here is a group of balls. Draw 1 loop around the blue ball and 1 loop around the green balls.

$\frac{1}{4}$ of the balls are blue

$\frac{3}{4}$ of the balls are green

$\frac{1}{4}$ + $\frac{3}{4}$ = 1

Here is a group of teddy bears. Draw 1 loop around the grey bears and 1 loop around the brown bears.

$\frac{1}{4}$ of the bears are grey

$\frac{3}{4}$ of the bears are brown

$\frac{1}{4}$ + $\frac{3}{4}$ = 1

Here is a group of cars. Draw 1 loop around the black cars and 1 loop around the pink cars.

of the cars are black

of the cars are pink

+ = 1

Well done!

Here is a group of yo-yos.

Draw 1 loop around the red yo-yos and 1 loop around the blue yo-yos.

 of the yo-yos are red

 of the yo-yos are blue

$\frac{1}{4} + \frac{3}{4} = 1$

If we put the yo-yos together we will have one whole group.

Here is a group of dinosaurs.

Draw a loop around a quarter (1 fourth) of them to fill in the red box below.

$\frac{1}{4}$ of 8 =

Then wipe your first loop away and do the same for these fractions.

$\frac{3}{4}$ of 8 =

$\frac{2}{4}$ of 8 =

What do you notice about $\frac{2}{4}$?

$\frac{2}{4}$ =

Here is a group of balls.

Draw a loop around a quarter (1 fourth) of them to fill in the red box below.

$\frac{1}{4}$ of 12 =

Then wipe your first loop away and do the same for these fractions.

$\frac{3}{4}$ of 12 =

$\frac{2}{4}$ of 12 =

What do you notice about $\frac{2}{4}$?

$\frac{2}{4}$ = _____

Here is a group of rockets.

Then wipe your first loop away and do the same for these fractions.

Draw a loop around a quarter (1 fourth) of them to fill in the red box below.

$\frac{1}{4}$ of 16 =

$\frac{3}{4}$ of 16 =

$\frac{2}{4}$ of 16 =

$\frac{2}{4}$ = _____

Well done!

Tick the shapes that show $\frac{1}{4}$.

62

Shade $\frac{1}{4}$ of each of these shapes.

Well done!

Write the correct numbers in the bar models to help you answer all the questions on these two pages.

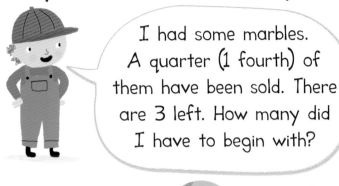

I had some marbles. A quarter (1 fourth) of them have been sold. There are 3 left. How many did I have to begin with?

4			
S	1	1	1

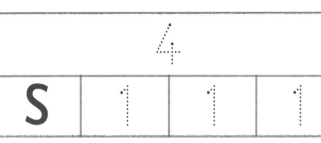

'S' stands for sold. If there are three left, each quarter is one. Tom had 4 marbles.

What if $\frac{1}{4}$ of the marbles were sold and there were 6 left?

Fill in this bar model and write your answer in the box. Wipe the bar model and box clean to answer the next question.

S			

☐ marbles were sold.

What if $\frac{1}{4}$ of the marbles were sold and there were 9 left?

Fill in this bar model to help you solve the first problem below. Write your answer in the red box. Then wipe them clean and use them to answer the next question.

| S | S | S | |

You can use this space to draw marbles to help you.

☐ marbles were left.

What if 12 of the marbles were sold and there were $\frac{1}{4}$ left?

What if 15 of the marbles were sold and there were $\frac{1}{4}$ left?

Make up a number of marbles that have been sold. There are $\frac{1}{4}$ left – how many is that?

☐ marbles were sold.

| | | | |

☐ marbles were left.

Well done!

Use the bar model to help you answer the questions on this page. Wipe it clean between questions.

I used a quarter (1 fourth) of my blocks to make a tower. I needed 4 blocks. How many did I start with?

$4 = \frac{1}{4}$ of ☐

You can use this space to draw blocks to help you.

I have 20 blocks, and I've used a quarter (1 fourth) of them to make a tower. How many did I use?

$\frac{1}{4}$ of 20 = ☐

Use a ruler to draw a string for each yo-yo that is the correct length.

$\frac{1}{4}$ of 4 centimetres

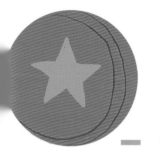
$\frac{1}{4}$ of 8 centimetres

$\frac{1}{4}$ of 12 centimetres

$\frac{1}{4}$ of 16 centimetres

$\frac{1}{4}$ of 20 centimetres

Well done! ⋰

This is a fraction wall. You can make one yourself using 3 equal-length strips of paper.

1️⃣ Keep one strip whole.

2️⃣ Fold one in half. Label each part $\frac{1}{2}$.

3️⃣ Fold the last one in half and half again. Label each part $\frac{1}{4}$.

1			
$\frac{1}{2}$		$\frac{1}{2}$	
$\frac{1}{4}$	$\frac{1}{4}$	$\frac{1}{4}$	$\frac{1}{4}$

Use the fraction wall to complete these:

$\frac{1}{2} + \frac{1}{2} = \boxed{}$ $1 - \boxed{} = \frac{1}{2}$

$\frac{1}{4} + \frac{3}{4} = \boxed{}$ $1 - \boxed{} = \frac{1}{4}$

$\frac{1}{2} + \frac{1}{4} = \boxed{}$ $\frac{3}{4} + \boxed{} = 1$

$\boxed{} - \frac{1}{4} = \frac{3}{4}$ $\boxed{} - \frac{3}{4} = \frac{1}{4}$

68

We know $\frac{1}{2}$ is one of 2 equal parts of a whole.

We know $\frac{1}{4}$ is one of 4 equal parts of a whole.

Write one of 3 equal parts. ☐

Write one of 5 equal parts. ☐

Write one of 6 equal parts. ☐

Write one of 7 equal parts. ☐

Write one of 8 equal parts. ☐

Well done!

69

SHAPES

A shape can be two-dimensional (2D) or three-dimensional (3D).

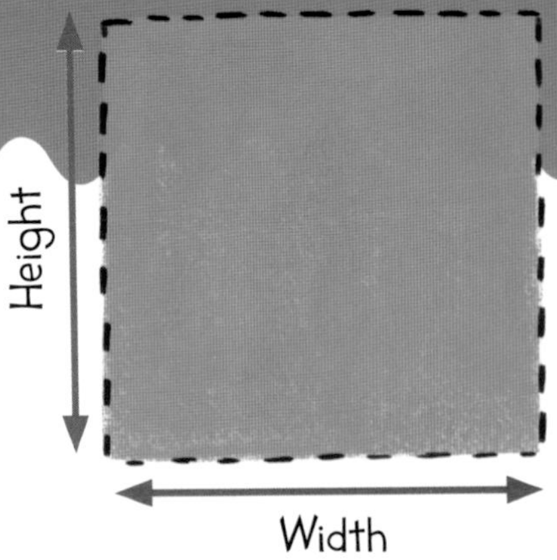

Height

Width

2D shapes

If a shape is 2D, it is completely flat. 2D shapes only have two dimensions — width and height.

2D SHAPES

NON-POLYGONS have one or more sides that aren't straight. Circles aren't polygons because they have no straight sides

POLYGONS have straight sides

TRIANGLES are polygons with 3 straight sides and 3 corners

QUADRILATERALS are polygons with 4 straight sides and 4 corners

OTHER POLYGONS have more than 4 straight sides, such as pentagons (5 sides)

RECTANGLES are *quadrilaterals* in which the corners are *right angles*. If they have two opposite sides that are shorter than the other two then they are called oblongs.

SQUARES are rectangles in which all sides are equal length

Trace the dotted lines to start drawing shapes!

Find out more about any words shown here in *bold* in the glossary on page 91.

3D shapes

A 3D shape has one more dimension than a 2D shape: depth (thickness). 3D shapes are often thought of as solid, but they can also be hollow, like an empty box.

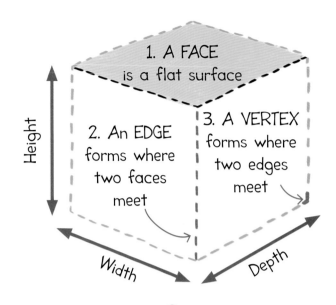

Height
Width
Depth

1. A FACE is a flat surface

2. An EDGE forms where two faces meet

3. A VERTEX forms where two edges meet

3D SHAPES

NON-POLYHEDRONS have at least one face that is not flat. Cylinders are non-polyhedrons

POLYHEDRONS have faces, edges and vertices

PRISMS are polyhedrons with matching ends, and faces that are parallelograms (*quadrilaterals* with opposite sides that are *parallel*)

PYRAMIDS are polyhedrons with a polygon base and faces that meet at an *apex*

TRIANGULAR PRISMS are prisms with 2 triangular faces joined by 3 rectangular faces

CUBOIDS are prisms with 6 flat faces that are rectangles

CUBES are cuboids with 6 square faces

Well done!

Spheres

How many yellow spheres can you see?

If an object is shaped like a sphere, we say it is 'spherical'.

Fill in the bottom bar for spheres, then wipe it clean and do it again for hemispheres.

Balls are often spherical. Draw around the ball that isn't a sphere.

Spheres and hemispheres

How many curved surfaces?

How many curved edges?

72

How many bubbles can you count?

If we cut a sphere in half, each half is called a hemisphere.

Trace the lines to draw the curved surfaces on the hemispheres.

How many circular faces?

Well done!

Cones and cylinders

Trace the lines to form the **apexes** of these cones.

How many yellow **conical** turrets can you see on the castle?

Is a cone a polyhedron?

Yes

No

We call cone-shaped objects, like my hat, 'conical'. Can you find my sister and draw around her matching hat?

Fill in the bottom bar for cones, then wipe it clean and do it again for cylinders.

Cones and cylinders

How many curved surfaces?

How many curved edges?

74

Trace the lines to draw one **face** of these cylinders.

How many **cylindrical** towers can you see?

If an object is shaped like a cylinder, we say it is 'cylindrical'.

How many circular faces?

Well done!

75

Cuboids

Colour inside the dotted lines to shade one **face** of these cuboids.

How many orange **cuboids** can you see?

Lots of boxes are cuboid-shaped. How many cuboids can you find in your house?

Cuboids

How many faces?

How many edges?

Trace the lines to draw one **face** of the cube.

Find the present that contains a **cube** and draw around it.

A cuboid is a type of prism.

A cube is a special cuboid — all of its faces are squares.

How many vertices?

Well done!

Other prisms

Colour inside the dotted lines to shade one **face** of these prisms.

How many purple **prisms** can you find? ☐

All prisms have ends that are joined by rectangles.

Prisms and pyramids

How many faces? ☐   How many edges? ☐

Pyramids

How many sides do the bases of these three pyramids have?

Fill in the bottom bar for prisms, then wipe it clean and do it again for pyramids.

All pyramids have triangular sides, but their bases can be different shapes.

How many vertices?

Well done!

79

Circles

Trace the lines on the circle I'm balancing on.

How many
red circles
can you see?

Circles

How many corners?

Half a circle is called a semi-circle.

Is a circle a polygon?

Yes

No

Well done!

Triangles

How many grey triangles can you see?

All three-sided shapes are triangles.

Trace the lines on my back to turn 4 triangles into 8.

Triangles

How many sides?

Is a triangle a polygon?

Yes

No

Trace all the triangles on me.

How many corners?

Well done!

83

Quadrilaterals

How many green quadrilaterals can you see?

Is a quadrilateral a polygon?

Yes   No

Quadrilaterals have no curved sides.

Quadrilaterals

How many sides?

Tick the shapes that are **quadrilaterals**:

Triangle ☐

Rectangle ☐

Square ☐

All four-sided shapes are quadrilaterals.

Trace the dotted lines to finish the tower.

How many corners? ☐

Well done!

85

Rectangles

Trace the lines to draw the bird wings that are at **right angles.**

How many **yellow oblongs** can you see?

An oblong's opposite sides are matching lengths.

Rectangles

How many sides?

Is a rectangle a polygon? (Yes) (No)

A square is a type of rectangle, because its corners are all right angles.

How many **purple squares** can you see?

A square is a quadrilateral in which all sides are the same length. Squares are sometimes called regular quadrilaterals.

How many corners?

Well done!

More than 4 sides

How many pink pentagons can you see?

Pentagons in which all sides are the same length are called 'regular pentagons'.

Fill in the bottom bar for pentagons, then wipe it clean and do it again for hexagons.

The black patches on a football are pentagons.

Pentagons and hexagons

How many sides?

Draw around the irregular hexagons.

How many orange hexagons can you see?

Bees build honeycombs that are perfectly hexagonal.

How many sides do these shapes have?

Heptagon

Octagon

Nonagon

How many corners?

Well done!

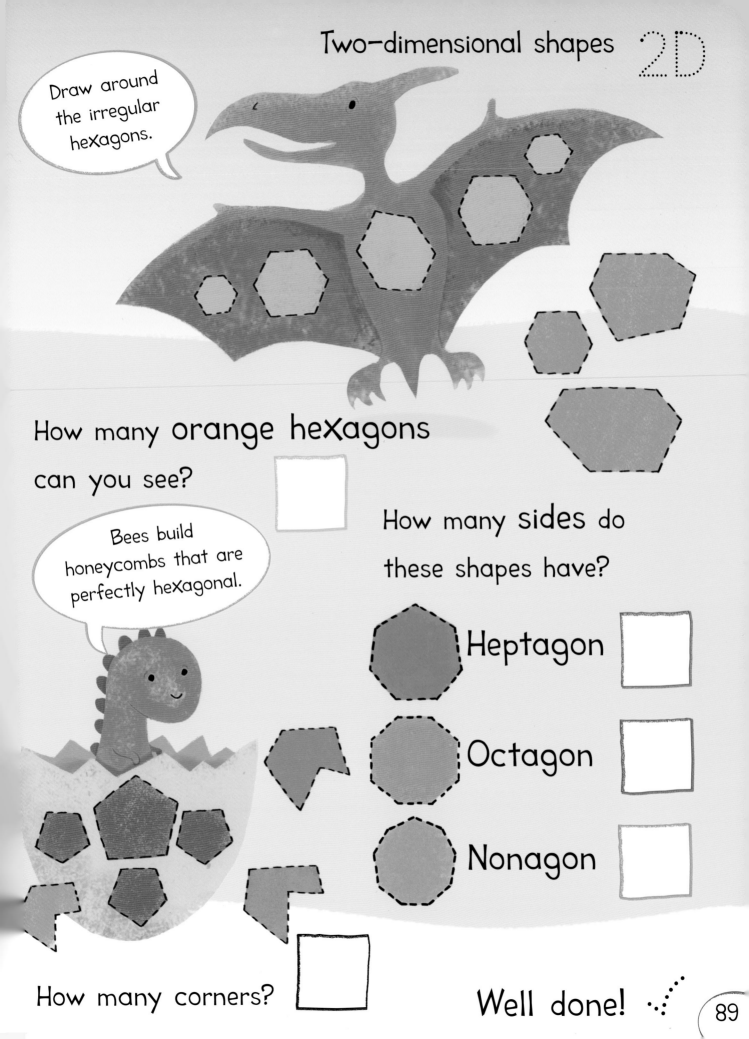

Index of shapes

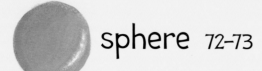

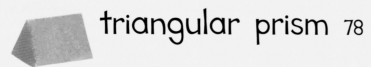

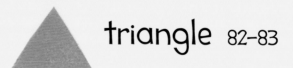

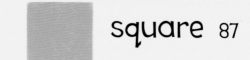
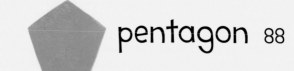

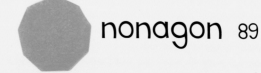

Glossary

apex — the point that forms the tip of a 3D shape, such as a cone or a pyramid.

parallel — two lines that will never meet, no matter how far they are extended.

parallelogram — quadrilaterals with opposite sides that are parallel

polygon — a 2D shape with no curved sides.

polyhedron — a 3D shape with no curved faces or edges.

quadrilateral — a four-sided polygon.

right angle — the angle between two lines is the amount you have to turn if you point along one line and then turn to point along the other. A quarter-turn is called a right angle.

More activities

Shape hunt Look around your house for objects that are 3D shapes. Search for all the 3D shapes in this book.

Sort your shapes Group the shapes you find into categories, such as number of faces, or whether their surfaces are curved, straight, or both. How many ways to sort can you think of?

Slide or roll? 3D shapes with flat faces can slide down a ramp. Those with curved surfaces can roll. Ask an adult to help you test this with objects from around your home.

Model shapes Try making 3D shapes out of modelling clay — look at the pictures in this book to help you.

Well done! .·´

Can you remember?

Memorising your times tables will save you all sorts of time. Use these tables to test yourself.

×1

1	x	1	=	1
2	x	1	=	2
3	x	1	=	3
4	x	1	=	4
5	x	1	=	5
6	x	1	=	6
7	x	1	=	7
8	x	1	=	8
9	x	1	=	9
10	x	1	=	10
11	x	1	=	11
12	x	1	=	12

×2

1	x	2	=	2
2	x	2	=	4
3	x	2	=	6
4	x	2	=	8
5	x	2	=	10
6	x	2	=	12
7	x	2	=	14
8	x	2	=	16
9	x	2	=	18
10	x	2	=	20
11	x	2	=	22
12	x	2	=	24

×5

1	x	5	=	5
2	x	5	=	10
3	x	5	=	15
4	x	5	=	20
5	x	5	=	25
6	x	5	=	30
7	x	5	=	35
8	x	5	=	40
9	x	5	=	45
10	x	5	=	50
11	x	5	=	55
12	x	5	=	60

×10

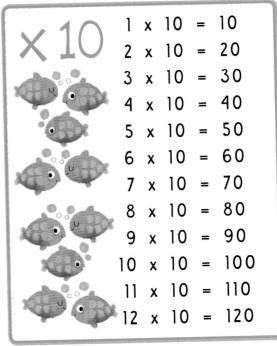

1	x	10	=	10
2	x	10	=	20
3	x	10	=	30
4	x	10	=	40
5	x	10	=	50
6	x	10	=	60
7	x	10	=	70
8	x	10	=	80
9	x	10	=	90
10	x	10	=	100
11	x	10	=	110
12	x	10	=	120

Hooray! You know your 1, 2, 5 and 10 times tables.

Fill in the bar models to solve the missing number problems.

1
7

$1 + \boxed{} = 7$

4 | 12

$4 + 12 = \boxed{}$

| | 11
15

$15 - 11 = \boxed{}$

9 |
14

$14 - 9 = \boxed{}$

3 | 12

$3 + 12 = \boxed{}$

Hooray! You can use bar models.

Hooray! You can colour fractions.

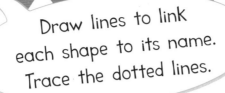

Draw lines to link each shape to its name. Trace the dotted lines.

cube

circle

pyramid

triangle

cylinder

triangular prism

pentagon

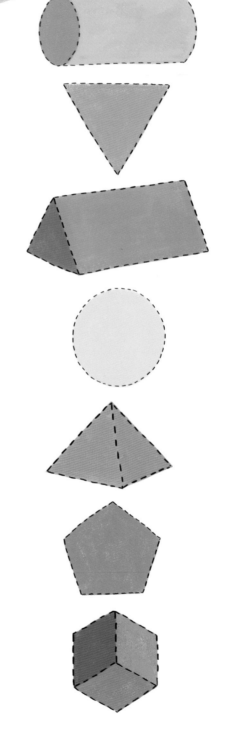

Hooray! You know your shapes.

Get Set Go Mathematics

Packed with wipe-clean activities to help your child enjoy maths!

Young learners will love exploring times tables, problem solving, fractions and shapes with cute characters and engaging activities. Wipe-clean pages mean exercises can be repeated again and again.

Activities to complete on every page

Bright illustrations

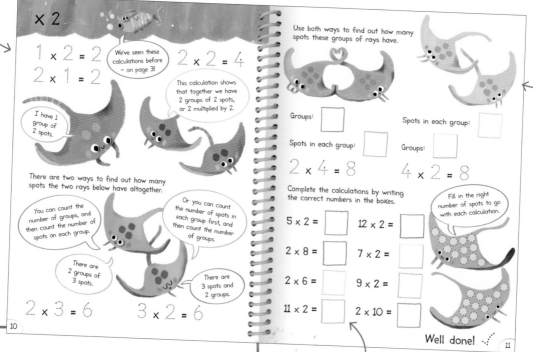

Wipe-clean pages mean no worries about mistakes

About the consultant

Caroline Clissold was a consultant and regional co-ordinator for the National Centre for Excellence in the Teaching of Mathematics, and supports teaching and learning in various schools. Her creative approach to teaching encourages children to apply their maths skills in meaningful contexts.

ISBN 978-1-78617-827-5

9 781786 178275

UK £12.99/US $14.95

Printed in China, Jun 2019, G96M19

Explore the whole Get Set Go range at
www.MilesKelly.net